Making Connections
Technology & Society

Science Interactions

Course 1

GLENCOE
Macmillan/McGraw-Hill
New York, New York   Columbus, Ohio   Mission Hills, California   Peoria, Illinois

A Glencoe Program

Science Interactions

Student Edition
Teacher Wraparound Edition
Science Discovery Activities: SE
Science Discovery Activities: TE
Teacher Classroom Resources
Laboratory Manual: SE
Laboratory Manual: TAE
Study Guide: SE
Study Guide: TE
Transparency Package
Computer Test Bank
Performance Assessment
Spanish Resources
Science and Technology Videodisc Series
Science and Technology Videodisc Teacher Guide
Integrated Science Videodisc Program

Send all inquiries to:
GLENCOE DIVISION
Macmillan/McGraw-Hill
936 Eastwind Drive
Westerville, Ohio 43081

ISBN 0-02-826769-9

Printed in the United States of America.

4 5 6 7 8 9 10 11 12 BAW 04 03 02 01 00 99 98 97 96

TABLE OF CONTENTS

To the Teacher 4

Chapter 1 Northwest Passage Controversy 5
Chapter 2 Fluorescent Light 7
Chapter 3 Telephones 9
Chapter 4 Institute of Standards and Technology 11
Chapter 5 Smog 13
Chapter 6 Cleaning Coal 15
Chapter 7 Environmental Change and Adaptation 17
Chapter 8 Who Should Be Allowed To Manufacture AZT? 19
Chapter 9 Better Ways to Battle Bugs 21
Chapter 10 Making Paper 23
Chapter 11 No-Till Farming 25
Chapter 12 Should School Buses Have Seat Belts? 27
Chapter 13 Space Law 29
Chapter 14 Protecting an Aquifer 31
Chapter 15 Shoreline Erosion 33
Chapter 16 The Harlequin Duck—An Environmental Indicator 35
Chapter 17 Weather Forecasting with Radar 37
Chapter 18 Measuring Earth Movements with Lasers 39
Chapter 19 Mariculture in the Bay of Fundy 41

TO THE TEACHER

The Making Connections: Technology and Society worksheets in *Science Interactions: Course 1*, deal with the impact of current scientific research and technologies on society. One of two types of worksheets will be provided for each chapter of *Science Interactions.* The worksheets titled Society will give factual information concerning a societal issue. The What Do You Think? feature at the end of each issue gives students the opportunity to answer questions designed to stimulate thought and conclusions related to the issue. The worksheets titled Technology will present current research or a technology that ties to concepts in the chapter. These worksheets will ask students to answer questions or interpret diagrams related to the topic. Connections Teacher Information follows each student worksheet. In it, you will find complete information for using these worksheets as a lesson. Purpose(s), Background, Teaching Strategies, Answers to Student Questions and a Wrap-up are provided for each worksheet.

NAME ______________________ DATE ______________ CLASS ______________

MAKING CONNECTIONS

Society

Chapter 1

Northwest Passage Controversy

Soon after Christopher Columbus had found land unknown to Europeans, other explorers started looking for a way around the land. The search began for a waterway, a northwest passage, across North America. It was nearly four hundred years before one was discovered.

Until recently, only the Inuit people cared about the area around the Northwest Passage. The Inuit live, hunt, and fish there. Today, however, other people are interested in the area because oil is plentiful there. Hundreds of oil wells have been drilled. Pipelines for oil and natural gas have been built, along with oil rig platforms, U.S. weather stations, and U.S. military bases. Also, specially built ships called icebreakers lead other ships that carry supplies to workers.

These changes have caused controversy. The United States says that this region is an international waterway. Any country has a right to sail through it or fly over it. Canada claims that the waters are part of the waterways between its islands. Therefore, it has authority over the air space above it and over the use of the waterways. It also claims rights to the minerals found there, including gas and oil. Canada and the United States have had a friendly relationship for almost two hundred years. In this dispute, the United States has agreed to ask Canada's permission to use the waterways. Canada has always granted it. But neither nation really thinks the other has the right to the waterways.

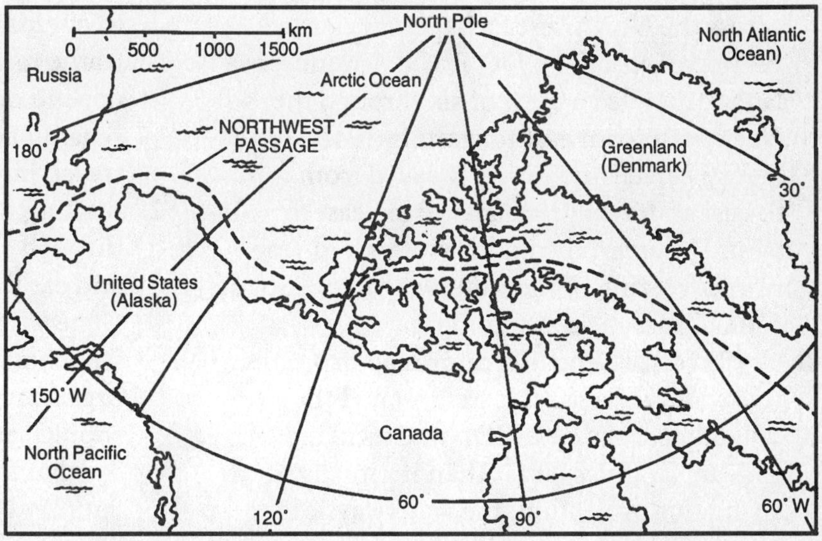

What Do You Think?

1. How might increased traffic affect the Inuit in the Northwest Passage? ______________________

2. How might Canadians benefit from the United States being in the Northwest Passage area?

3. How should debates about international waterways be decided? Explain your answer.

Use with Chapter 1, Section 1:1

Purpose

- The purpose of this connection is to help students realize that geographic features are important as both physical features and political features.

Motivate

- Five hundred years ago, Columbus thought he could reach Asia by sailing west. On a globe, trace a westward path from Spain to the Americas. Ask students what they would do if they were confronted with a land obstacle in their search for a route to Asia.

Background

- It was not until the early 1900s that a route across the Northwest Passage was charted. Between 1903 and 1906, Roald Amundsen, a Norwegian, led a crew of six through the Northwest from east to west. In 1942, Henry Larsen and his crew sailed from west to east and, two years later, from east to west. However, the bitter winters and year-round freezing of the waterway made such a route impractical at that time.
- Until recently, the Mercator map projection was widely accepted. It exaggerated the size of land near the poles. On it, Greenland appears 16 times larger than it actually is. Using this projection, the waterways of the Northwest look very wide, like an international passage.
- In 1988, the National Geographic Society adopted the Robinson projection. It is an improved picture of the Earth with a better balance of size and shape. This projection favors the Canadian point of view, because the passage appears much smaller.

Teaching Strategies

- Discuss landforms and other geographical features that divide states. Look at a map and have students point out the different states that are bounded by the Mississippi River.
- Talk about boundaries between the United States and Canada. Look at the boundaries on a map.
- Note that maps can't always show geographical features accurately. The problem is that the Earth is a sphere, and mapmakers must draw it on a flat piece of paper. The size of features and the actual shapes are sometimes distorted.

Answers to Student Worksheet

1. **Recognizing cause and effect:** Increased traffic might scare wild game that the Inuit depend on for food. Icebreakers could separate ice flows over which the Inuit travel, interrupting hunting or travel.
2. **Making inferences:** Canada might benefit through shared data from weather stations and early warning from defense bases.
3. **Generating and assessing solutions:** Some students may say that an international organization, such as the United Nations, should settle disputes. Other students may say that the decision should be made by a country bordering the waterway. Accept any answers that are logically supported.

Wrap-up

- Summarize with the class the points of view of the United States and Canada. Discuss how people living in the area might feel. Have the students choose a controversial topic, divide into two groups, and debate the issue. Then have each side debate the same issue from the other group's point of view.

NAME ____________________ DATE ____________ CLASS ____________

MAKING CONNECTIONS

Society

Chapter 2

Fluorescent Light

Most light bulbs used in the home are incandescent bulbs. These bulbs give off light because electricity makes the filament inside so hot that it glows. But only 10 percent of the electricity used becomes light. The majority of the electricity becomes heat.

A more energy-efficient way to produce light is with fluorescent bulbs. These bulbs use less energy and usually last much longer than incandescent bulbs. Fluorescent bulbs turn 20 percent of the electrical energy into light, twice as much as incandescent bulbs.

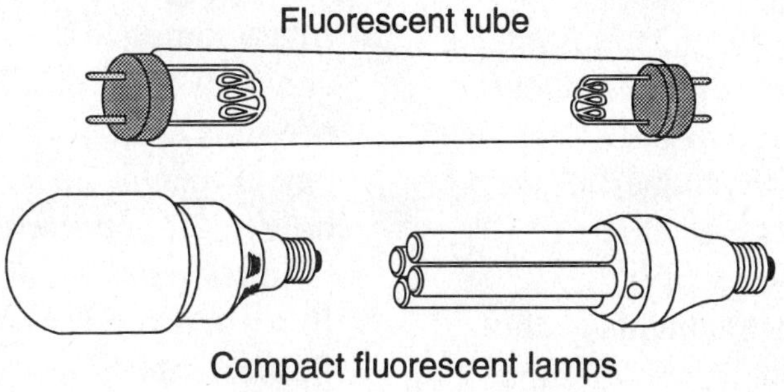

Fluorescent bulbs are tubes that contain a gas that is activated by electricity. The gas causes a coating in the bulb to produce light. These bulbs are used as ceiling lighting in most stores. Manufacturers are now producing them for lamps.

Saving energy is very important. Because fluorescent bulbs convert more electricity to light, a single fluorescent bulb can save around 500 pounds of coal over the life of the bulb. It would produce about one ton less of carbon dioxide and 21 pounds less of sulfur dioxide than an incandescent bulb. It would save about $50 in electricity over its lifetime of 10 000 hours.

If two-thirds of the incandescent bulbs in the United States were replaced, the results would be tremendous. There would be 200 million less tons of carbon dioxide produced and 20 million less tons of sulfur dioxide. It would also save 250 million barrels of oil.

Why aren't fluorescent bulbs used more? In the past, the long, narrow shape of most fluorescent bulbs limited their use to overhead lighting. Compact fluorescent bulbs have been developed that, although a little larger than most commonly used incandescent bulbs, fit most lamps and indoor lighting fixtures. Lamp manufacturers have begun to adapt their lamp shades to accommodate these new bulbs. However, fluorescent bulbs are more expensive, from a few cents to several dollars, depending on the size and applicaton.

Fluorescent bulbs are a good alternative for incandescent bulbs. They use less electricity and last longer. Since saving energy is so important, why not start using fluorescent bulbs in the home?

What Do You Think?

1. What are advantages and disadvantages of fluorescent bulbs? ____________________

____

____

2. If you replaced the incandescent bulbs in your home with fluorescent bulbs, how much money would you save on electricity during the life of the fluorescent bulbs? ____________________

____

Use with Chapter 2, Section 2:1

Purpose

- The purpose of this connection is to help students understand the difference between fluorescent and incandescent bulbs.

Motivate

- Have students count the number of incandescent bulbs in their homes. Have them determine how much less pollution would be produced if they used fluorescent bulbs instead of incandescent.

Background

- Incandescent bulbs were produced by Thomas Edison in 1879. They haven't changed much since then. By increasing the size of the filament, or using different gases, we have increased the life of the bulbs, but they are not that much more energy efficient than they were.
- In incandescent bulbs, the filaments get hot and evaporate. Newer incandescent lamps are the quartz-halogen lamps. There is a chamber that surrounds the filament and causes the tungsten from the filament to be redeposited onto the filament. This makes it burn more brightly and last longer. The quartz-halogen lamps are used in spotlights and for special lighting. They are also used in car headlights.
- Fluorescent bulbs were invented about 60 years after the incandescent bulbs and were used mostly as ceiling fixtures in stores or businesses. A device called a ballast helped start the light by sending a surge of electricity between the electrodes at each end of the bulb. This was one of the drawbacks in putting them in lamps that were designed for incandescent bulbs. Special ballasts have been designed that screw into the lamps or can be plugged into the wall sockets. The fluorescent bulbs then screw into the ballasts. Compact fluorescent bulbs have been developed that hold the ballast in the base of the bulb which fits into most standard lamps. Most lamps were not designed to hold the shapes of the fluorescent bulbs. New holders for the lamp shades usually need to be purchased.
- A disadvantage to manufacturers is that the fluorescent bulbs are long lasting. Turnover is low and profit margins are not as high. When electric companies have sold fluorescent fixtures at a discount, people did not buy them. Businesses have changed to fluorescent fixtures because energy savings are much more evident for them.

Teaching Strategies

- Invite someone from the local electric utility company to discuss local programs that promote switching to fluorescent technology. If there is no local program, find out how to get one started or why one has not been started.
- Bring in incandescent bulb packages and fluorescent bulb packages. Compare the wattage and the number of lumens. The wattage indicates how much energy is used by the bulb, and the lumens indicate how much light is produced. Which are the most efficient? Least efficient?

Answers to Student Worksheet

1. **Drawing conclusions:** Advantages—They produce more light, use less electricity, and cost less in the long run. Disadvantages—Their shape usually is not as convenient as that of incandescent bulbs, and they are slightly more expensive.
2. **Recognizing cause and effect:** Take the number of bulbs and multiply by $50. Example: 10 × $50 = $500.

Wrap-up

- Have students call stores that sell light bulbs and find out if they sell fluorescent bulbs and how much they cost. Also, ask students to find out the different kinds of fluorescent bulbs that are available. Students can present their results to the class.

NAME ______________________ DATE ______________ CLASS ______________

MAKING CONNECTIONS

Society

Chapter 3

Telephones

The invention of the telephone changed the world. Sending voices electronically allows people to communicate with each other over long distances in seconds. Since 1876, when the telephone was invented, it has become part of most people's lives. More than 600 million phones are used in the world. In the United States alone, there are over 181 million phones.

A variety of phones are available today. For example, speaker phones allow you to speak to more than one person in a room. Color videophones that work using standard telephone wiring let you see the person you are talking to. Some phones connect to a "fax" machine that copies drawings and reports and sends them over the telephone. Some phones can send information from one computer to another.

Not only are there many different kinds of phones, but there are many different places from which you can make your call. You can speak to someone from your home, from your back-yard, from a car, or even from a ship or airplane. A special undersea fiber-optic cable between Europe and North America can transfer at least 80 000 signals at the same time between the two continents. Satellites help in sending your voice from one part of the world to another. Special satellite dishes on Earth send telephone signals as high as 36 000 km and relay them to another dish on Earth.

Many businesses have been built around the telephone, from the factories that make telephones to the businesses that provide phone answering services. Operators, repair people, equipment designers, engineers, and phone book publishers are just some of the people who work in the telephone industry. In fact, over a million people in the United States depend on the telephone industry for their jobs.

What Do You Think?

1. How would your life be different without a telephone? ______________________

____

2. Why might a lumberjack be considered part of the telephone industry? Name another job, other than those mentioned in the reading, that might be part of the telephone industry.

____

____

CONNECTIONS TEACHER INFORMATION

Use with Chapter 3, Sections 3:1–3:3

Purpose

- The purpose of this connection is to help students understand the importance of the telephone to our society.
- Students should also understand that people in a variety of fields depend on the telephone industry for their livelihoods.

Motivate

- List student suggestions of the different ways people use the telephone in their lives.
- Ask students why they think companies give directories to their customers.

Background

- Alexander Graham Bell, who emigrated from Scotland to the United States, invented the telephone. On March 10, 1876, while working on his invention, he spilled acid on himself. This caused him to exclaim to his assistant, Thomas Watson, who was in another room, the now famous words: "Mr. Watson, come here, I want you!" Watson came running to tell Mr. Bell that he had heard him clearly.
- There are more telephones in the United States than in any other country—more than 181 million. Japan and Germany are second and third in the number of telephones in use—about 66 million and 45 million, respectively.
- In the United States, phone companies are owned and run by private businesses. In other countries, such as Italy, Sweden, and Peru, the government owns and runs them. And in still other countries, like Denmark and Finland, the government and private companies each play a part in ownership and operation.

Teaching Strategies

- Explain how Alexander Graham Bell invented the telephone, and discuss how the process of inventing depends on hard work, research, and perseverance.
- Talk about how we take certain things in our lives for granted—such as the telephone, electric lights, running water, washing machines, etc.

Answers to Student Worksheet

1. **Developing a perspective:** Students might say that they would have to walk to visit a friend or relay a message rather than use the phone, or that they would have to look for a police officer in order to summon help in an emergency.
2. **Making inferences, predictions, and interpretations:** A lumberjack cuts down trees that are used for telephone poles. Other jobs in the telephone industry include satellite designers, secretaries, mathematicians, company doctors, nurses, people who prepare phone bills.

Wrap-up

- Conclude the activity by discussing how operators can provide emergency help and how implementing the 911 system has saved lives.

NAME ______________________ DATE ______________ CLASS ______________

MAKING CONNECTIONS
Society

Chapter 4

Institute of Standards and Technology

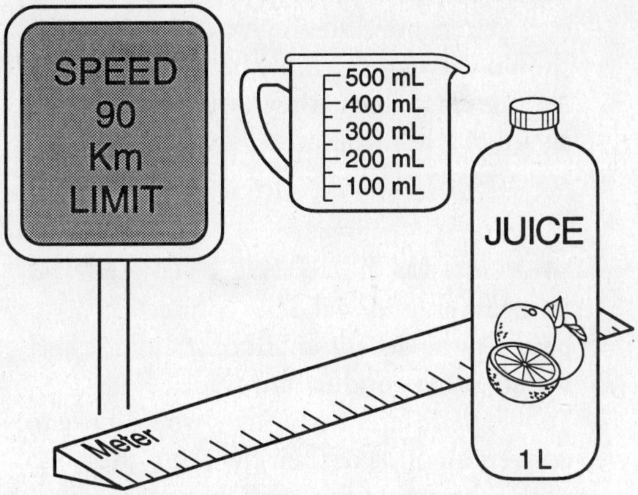

Can you show exactly how long a centimeter is? How much do you weigh? How can you be so sure? Are all rulers and scales the same? What about clocks? If you can't trust your ruler, how can you measure anything?

Somewhere, someone must know exactly how long a centimeter is. That "somewhere" is the National Institute of Standards and Technology in Gaithersburg, Maryland. There, scientists keep the information necessary to demonstrate consistently the masses, distances, and times on which our measurements are based.

Scientists have greatly refined the standards of measurement in recent years. They have found that some behaviors occur the same way time after time, making them useful for establishing reliable standards of measurement. The official definition of a meter is based on the distance traveled by light in a certain period of time. A second is defined by the number of vibrations of an atom of cesium metal. A kilogram equals the mass of a special metal cylinder kept at the International Bureau of Weights and Measures near Paris, France. The bureau includes members from 46 countries.

How can importers be sure that one kilogram of sugar from Costa Rica is the same as one kilogram of sugar in the United States? If there were no standards of mass, time, and distance, people might never stop arguing over matters of business.

What Do You Think?

1. The Commerce Department oversees the National Institute of Standards and Technology. Why do you suppose this is? ______________________

____

____

____

2. What problems do you think there would be with international trade if countries disagreed on measurement systems? ______________________

____

____

____

Use with Chapter 4, Section 4:2

Purpose

- The purpose of this connection is to show students the importance of standard measurement.

Motivate

- Without any standard measuring devices, have students demonstrate their ability to estimate the size of the classroom, their height, the weight of a book, and the time it takes someone to walk one block.

Background

- The metric system was developed to simplify mathematical operations involving measurements. The history of weights and measures includes many bizarre standards which can be used to illustrate the need for a system of standards. The English, or customary, system is a nightmare to work with mathematically. The cubit, a unit of length used in ancient times, was the distance from a man's elbow to the tip of his middle finger. The Egyptians used sun clocks to measure time. The Romans used a unit called the *uncia*, which equaled the width of a thumb. A foot, based roughly on the length of a man's foot, equaled 12 uncia. A yard was approximately the distance from a man's nose to the tip of the middle finger.

Teaching Strategies

- To show the need for standards and to demonstrate the inadequacy of the old measurement systems, have the largest and smallest members of the class compare the distance from their nose to the tip of their outstretched middle finger. The distances should vary considerably between students. Ask the class whom they would want to buy a yard of cloth from, the biggest or the smallest?

Answers to Student Worksheet

1. Students should make the connection between the development of standards and the ability to conduct fair trade.
2. People in different countries would have to convert all units of their own into the units of the country with which they are trading. Time would be lost getting perishables through customs, many kinds of measuring equipment would be needed, and arguments might hinder trade relations.

Wrap-up

- Check the students' estimates in the Motivate section by using a set of standard measurement devices. Point out that if two students were building a school, for example, and their measurements disagreed by even a centimeter, it could make walls uneven and affect the rest of the building. Only by using a standard set of measurement devices can people agree on distances, weights, time, and sizes.

NAME ______________________ DATE ______________ CLASS ______________

MAKING CONNECTIONS

Society

Chapter 5

Smog

Smog is a solution of gases we would be happy to live without. The term "smog" was first used to indicate a combination of *smoke* and *fog* found in large cities. Today the term also refers to conditions caused by various pollutants, other than smoke, that react with sunlight. Since heat from sunlight helps produce smog, smog is more of a problem during warm weather.

Most of the pollutants that cause smog come from the exhaust of automobiles and trucks and from factory emissions. However, many other things also contribute to smog. Among them are gasoline-powered lawn mowers, starter fluids for barbecue grills, household cleaning solvents, oil-based paints, and spray cans that contain hairspray or deodorant.

Smog is a worldwide problem. European cities, such as Rome and Budapest, are so troubled with smog they have banned cars from their city centers. In the spring of 1992, the schools in Mexico City were closed for several weeks to keep the children from having to be out in the smog-filled air. And although smog is worse in large cities, it is also found in areas far from the cities. Wind patterns, for example, can carry pollutants far from their source to inconvenience or even harm plant and animal life in other areas.

Countries all over the world are developing laws and regulations to help reduce air pollution. Some of these regulations deal with the automobile industry, requiring carmakers to produce cars that get better gas mileage or use a different kind of gasoline and give off less pollutants. Other laws regulate the use of charcoal lighter fluids, oil-based paints, and aerosol cans.

What Do You Think?

1. How could you change your lifestyle to help cut down on air pollution? ______________________

____

____

2. Why is smog usually worse in large cities than in the country? ______________________

____

____

____

3. Why does smog occur in the open country as well as large cities? ______________________

____

____

____

CONNECTIONS TEACHER INFORMATION

Use with Chapter 5, Section 5:1

Purpose

- The purpose of this connection is to help the students understand what causes smog and the problems that smog causes.

Motivate

- Have students discuss how automobile pollution could be controlled. Include suggestions such as mandating increased gas mileage, incorporating flex-time in work schedules to cut down on increased idling time due to traffic congestion, encouraging greater use of bicycles or mass transit, carpooling, and using ethanol as fuel for cars.

Background

- Smog-causing pollutants contain chemicals called hydrocarbons. When hydrocarbons combine with nitrogen oxides and are heated in the sunlight, ozone is formed.
- Smog is a health hazard for everyone, but it is particularly dangerous for children and for those suffering from respiratory diseases. Lead in the pollutants poses a special danger to children. The lead is inhaled or ingested and accumulates in bones and other tissues. While children's nervous systems are still developing, the lead can cause irreversible brain or nerve damage. It can also damage the kidneys.

Teaching Strategies

- Explain that smog is formed by pollutants reacting with the air as they are heated in sunlight.
- Discuss various sources of pollutants that cause smog. Mention the largest contributors, automobiles and factories, but also emphasize those sources that the students may use, such as aerosol cans.
- Discuss the worldwide problem of smog and the regulations that are needed to cut down on it.

Answers to Student Worksheet

1. **Generating and assessing solutions:** Students might suggest switching to pump hair spray and roll-on deodorant, or riding bikes, walking, or taking public transportation rather than asking parents to drive them.
2. **Drawing conclusions:** There are many more vehicles in large cities than in other areas, and they cause much of the pollution.
3. **Recognizing cause and effect:** The winds transport pollution all around the world.

Wrap-up

- As a class, write a letter to the editor of the local newspaper, telling people what they can do to curtail air pollution.
- Develop a problem. Ask whether it would be better for 40 people to ride a public transportation bus or to drive 40 private cars. Assume the bus travels 50 miles and gets four miles per gallon of gasoline. Each car drives 10 miles and gets 20 miles per gallon. Each gallon of gasoline produces the same amount of pollutants in each vehicle. Which scenario would produce less smog?

  For the bus:

  $50 \text{ mi} \div 4 \text{ mi/gal} = 12.5 \text{ gal}$ used by bus

  For the cars:

  $10 \text{ mi} \div 20 \text{ mi/gal} = 0.5 \text{ gal}$ used by each car $\times$ 40 cars $= 20$ gal total

  The bus uses less fuel, so it will produce less smog.

NAME ____________________ DATE ____________ CLASS ____________

MAKING CONNECTIONS

Technology

Chapter 6

Cleaning Coal

More than half of the electricity used in the United States is produced from coal. More than one-third of U.S. coal reserves are made up of medium- and high-sulfur coals. When burned, medium- and high-sulfur coals produce sulfur dioxide, which causes acid rain. Acid rain damages forests, kills fish in freshwater lakes, and erodes buildings and monuments. Current laws require utility companies to reduce sulfur dioxide emissions. How this will be done is the subject of much debate.

Sulfur content of coals

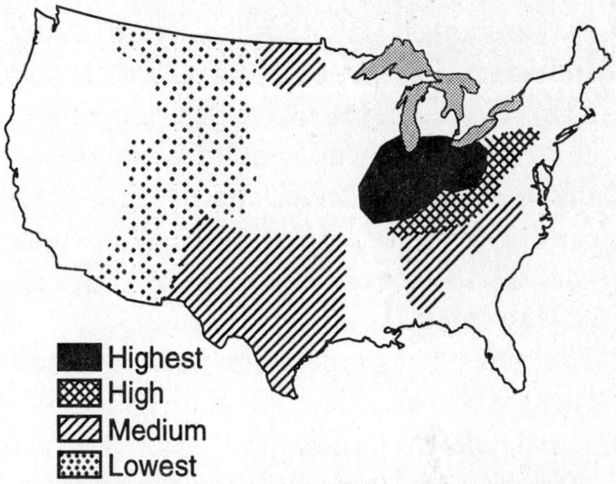

Technology currently used to reduce sulfur dioxide emissions uses flue gas scrubbers. These scrubbers are large chemical devices that absorb sulfur dioxide fumes released when coal is burned. This process prevents sulfur dioxide from entering the atmosphere. But scrubbers use vast amounts of water and produce large quantities of waste called sludge. In addition, scrubbers require additional coal to power them.

Several new clean coal technologies have been developed. Some methods clean the coal before it is burned. Others change the way coal is burned to prevent harmful emissions from leaving the smokestacks.

One new method is called fluidized-bed combustion. Crushed coal is burned in a bed of limestone. The limestone prevents sulfur dioxide from forming. Water, circulated in metal coils through the limestone bed, is heated by the burning coal. The water changes to steam, which is then used to produce electricity.

Another promising method, integrated coal-gasification combined cycle, uses special turbines much like jet engines. These turbines are fueled by coal that has first been turned into gas. They are even more efficient in producing electricity when a second turbine is powered by stem produced from the hot exhaust gases of the first turbine.

Some new technologies are more energy efficient than the current technology. However, many of them will not be ready for wide-scale use until the late 1990s.

Thinking About Technology Connections

1. Should utility companies be allowed to wait until new clean coal devices are perfected, or should they be required to install scrubbers immediately? Explain your answer. ____________________

____

2. Do you think the United States should move toward cleaner sources of electricity, such as nuclear and hydropower? Why or why not? ____________________

____

CONNECTIONS TEACHER INFORMATION

Use with Chapter 6, Sections 6:1, 6:3

Purpose

- The purpose of this connection is to help students understand the issues surrounding cleaning coal.

Motivate

- Ask students if pollution is a serious issue and who should be responsible for cleaning it up. Ask students to decide whether the cost of coal clean-up should be built into the price charged for electricity. Encourage the beginning of a debate. (See Wrap-up.)

Background

- The states that produce the most high-sulfur coal are Illinois, Indiana, Ohio, and Missouri. Following these are Kentucky, West Virginia, and Pennsylvania. Tennessee, Alabama, Texas, North Dakota, Virginia, and New Mexico have a midrange sulfur content in their coal.
- There are many coal-cleaning methods currently being used. New methods are continually being developed. These methods vary according to the cost of changing the existing system, the cost of performance, the energy efficiency, the efficiency of removing pollutants, and the amount of waste that is left.

Teaching Strategies

- Integrated coal-gasification combined cycle power plants are capable of generating more electricity per ton of coal than conventional coal-burning plants. Through gasification, up to 99% of the coal's sulfur content can be removed. However, the gasification process adds substantially to the cost of operation.
- Identify areas in the United States that produce high-sulfur coal.
- Explain some different ways coal is cleaned and how these vary as to the cost, efficiency and amount of waste produced.

Answers to Student Worksheet

1. **Developing a perspective:** Students may differ in their opinion. Companies should be allowed to wait for new technology because it will result in cleaner and more efficient power production at less cost to the consumer. On the other hand, scrubbers should be installed immediately because acid rain is a problem that needs immediate attention.
2. **Developing a perspective:** Yes. It is important to have cleaner air and less acid rain. No. New technology could increase the price of electricity.

Wrap-up

- Return to the debate in the Motivate section. Have students identify different groups that would be affected by the issue of cleaning coal. These may include the utility producer, the utility user, environmental groups, and coal miners. Assign one or more students to each group and have them debate the issues surrounding burning high-sulfur coal and having to clean it. Ask the rest of the class who was most persuasive in the debate.

NAME ________________ DATE ________ CLASS ________

MAKING CONNECTIONS

Society

Chapter 7

Environmental Change and Adaptation

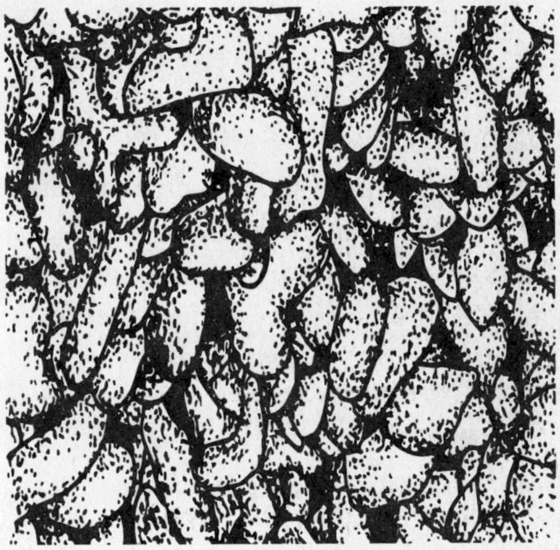

TB bacteria

A polar bear has thick, white fur that provides warmth and camouflage in polar regions. Ferns grow well in shady areas. Cacti have thick stems to store water in a hot, dry desert. Each species adapts to a particular environment and survives. If a species doesn't adapt, it dies out. The better the members of a species are adapted to the environment, the better the species' chance for survival.

But what happens to an organism when its environment changes? Usually, environmental changes occur slowly. In this case, adaptation proceeds slowly and is hard to observe. Sometimes, though, a change happens quickly, and so does adaptation. An example is the resistance of bacteria to antibiotics.

Throughout most of human history, people have both benefited and been harmed by bacteria. Most bacteria species help people, such as those that aid in the digestive process or cause milk to change into cheese. Some species of bacteria, however, cause disease.

Until recent times, people were not very successful in fighting harmful bacteria. But the development of antibiotics during the years of World War II provided an effective weapon against many diseases. Tuberculosis (TB), for example, showed a marked drop in reported cases throughout the world following the introduction of antibiotics. By the early 1990s, however, TB was making an alarming comeback.

During the years that TB was being fought with antibiotics, two things happened. Because the disease seemed to be conquered, drug companies stopped researching new remedies against TB. At the same time, however, the TB microbes were undergoing adaptations that enabled them to resist the drugs present in their environment. The number of cases of TB began to rise, and health officials found that antibiotics previously successful in fighting TB were no longer effective.

Because no two bacteria within the same species are exactly alike genetically, a few of the bacteria that cause a certain disease, such as TB, may contain genes that protect them from being destroyed by specific antibiotics. These bacteria are said to be *resistant.* The resistant organisms survive, reproduce, and increase their population. In this way, over time, the bacteria species adapts and develops into a tough, drug-resistant form, as seen in the TB-causing bacteria that are taking hold now.

Thinking About Technology Connections

1. Why might treatment with a variety of TB-fighting drugs be effective against new strains of TB bacteria? ________________

2. Drug companies often stop research on diseases that have been controlled. Explain why you agree or disagree with this practice. ________________

Use with Chapter 7, Section 7:1

Purpose

- The purpose of this connection is to demonstrate how environmental change can radically affect organisms, causing adaptations for living in the new environment.

Motivate

- Have students name specific diseases that are cured or prevented by medication. Ask students to speculate on ways life might be different if one or more of these medications were no longer available.

Background

- Although members of a particular species are very similar, genetic variations continually appear. It is the presence of these variations that enable a species to evolve over time. Organisms most suited to an environment outlive those that are less adapted.
- Today, staphylococcus (staph) are among the most drug-resistant bacteria. In 1994, scientists estimated that 40 percent of common hospital staph bacteria were resistant to all but one known antibiotic. Drug-resistant strains of bacteria causing pneumonia, blood poisoning, gonorrhea, meningitis, and syphilis all pose risks to world health.
- TB is transmitted through close physical contact, and people living in overcrowded quarters such as prisons and shelters for the homeless are at particular risk. Individuals infected with HIV are especially vulnerable to infectious diseases like TB. Since one in seven TB cases is now drug-resistant, health professionals worry that TB will become a major health problem for the whole population.
- Completing only part of a course of antibiotics (stopping your medication before you are supposed to) can lead to drug-resistant strains of bacteria. Killing off just some of the bacteria gives the remaining bacteria time to adapt. It is possible that this is the primary cause of drug-resistant TB. TB requires long-term (6 months to 15 months) treatment with antibiotics. Because the course of treatment extends over a long period, there is a good deal of noncompliance with this treatment regimen.
- Bacteria are not the only organisms that adapt to chemicals. DDT was once used all over the world to kill harmful insects. However, within a few years after its introduction, DDT-resistant insects emerged.

Teaching Strategies

- Since 1985, the worldwide incidence of TB has risen dramatically. In 1992, 2.9 million deaths were blamed on this disease. Ask students to infer how drug-resistant TB can lead to increased incidence of the disease. Explain that drug-resistant TB increases the mortality rate from the disease and allows infected but untreated individuals to transmit the disease to others. Students should understand that the bacterial species responsible for TB is gradually evolving to become drug-resistant as drug-resistant strains outlive weaker strains of the species.

Answers to Student Worksheet

1. **Making inferences:** Use of a variety of drugs might be more effective against TB since a bacteria might not be resistant to all the different remedies.
2. **Developing a perspective:** Possible answers: Agree—Once a disease is controlled, research should focus on other diseases. Disagree—Because of resistance, any disease can reemerge. New drugs must always be available to fight new strains.

Wrap-up

- Most livestock receive antibiotics to control disease. Antibiotics remain in the meat after the animal is slaughtered. Ask students to weigh both the possible benefits and drawbacks for the use of antibiotics in livestock.

MAKING CONNECTIONS

Society

Chapter 8

Who Should Be Allowed to Manufacture AZT?

In the fight against AIDS, acquired immune deficiency syndrome, scientists are searching for an effective antiviral medicine. This is a great challenge for several reasons. First, scientists have not been very successful in curing other viral diseases. Then too, the life cycle of the AIDS virus is complicated. In addition, HIV, the virus that causes AIDS, infects white blood cells of the immune system. These are cells your body uses to fight off illness. So, when a person becomes infected with HIV, other cells will destroy the HIV-infected white blood cells, which are viewed as pathogens. How can HIV be killed without further harming the body's immune system?

For several years, the only medicine licensed by the U.S. Food and Drug Administration (FDA) for the treatment of AIDS was zidovudine, usually called AZT. Now several additional medicines are licensed for AIDS treatment, including ddI (or dideoxyinosine or dideoxycytidine) and ddC (or zalcitabine). These medicines help to slow the progression of HIV and prolong the lives of some patients. These medicines also may delay the development of AIDS in some people who are infected with HIV but don't have any symptoms yet. Some research shows that giving AZT to pregnant women with AIDS may keep their unborn babies from developing the disease.

Scientists are currently studying more than 25 different medicines for the prevention and treatment of AIDS. Some of these medicines are designed to keep the virus from reproducing after it invades the body. Others, in the form of vaccines, are designed to cause the immune system to fight HIV. Because so few medicines have been shown to have any effect, AZT is in great demand.

Currently, a national drug company holds the patent for AZT in more than 40 countries. This means it is the only company that can legally manufacture AZT in those countries. AZT is extremely expensive. Many people believe the price of AZT would come down if other companies also were allowed to manufacture it. Some people believe that one company should not have sole right to a patent since much of the research that helped discover AZT was funded with government grants. In some countries where the company does not hold the patent, other drug companies sell AZT for much less money. Some people travel to these countries to buy AZT at the cheaper price.

What Do You Think?

1. Should only one company be allowed to hold a patent for AZT? Why or why not?

____

____

2. Should the government control prices for expensive medications like AZT? Who should pay the cost of developing new medications? ______________________

____

____

CONNECTIONS TEACHER INFORMATION

Use with Chapter 8, Section 8:1

Purpose

The purpose of this connection is to relate students' knowledge of viruses to a real-life, controversial issue involving the production of a medication for a frighteningly dangerous virus—the AIDS virus (HIV).

Motivate

- Involve students in a discussion about their knowledge of the AIDS virus, its causes and its consequences.
- Have students express their opinions about what the government's role should be in providing medications to people suffering from deadly diseases.

Background

- The AIDS virus is classified as a retrovirus. A retrovirus, in contrast to other viruses, carries its genetic code in RNA rather than DNA. The retrovirus uses its RNA to make DNA, a reversal of the usual process. This reversed process enables the retrovirus to become permanently embedded in the DNA of infected immune cells. The immune cells make more HIV themselves, and the body has no way to rid itself of the virus.
- HIV is a very poor replicator. That is, it mutates often when reproducing. This makes AIDS additionally difficult to control, since the virus mutates and becomes resistant to treatment.
- Medications to prevent and treat AIDS fall into three basic categories: drugs aimed at halting replication of HIV within the body, drugs aimed at the repair and enhancement of the infected immune system, and vaccines to prevent initial infection from the virus. Most experts believe that many different AIDS treatments and preventives will be necessary to halt the spread of the disease in its many forms and stages. Someday AIDS treatment may come from gene therapy. This technique would provide cells already infected with the AIDS virus with new, altered genes that inhibit production of new viruses.

Teaching Strategies

- Discuss the controversy surrounding the high cost of AZT and other medicines, and the patenting of medicines developed in part with government research grants.
- Discuss government funding of disease research and the social and economic implications of drugs that would cure so few people that private industry cannot afford to develop and produce them.

Answers to Student Worksheet

1. **Drawing conclusions:** Yes—If a company developed a medication, it should be allowed to patent it and benefit from its sale. No—The production of a medication should be permitted in as many companies as can safely produce it. This will make it readily available at as low a cost as possible. Accept all reasonable answers.
2. **Drawing conclusions:** Accept all reasonable answers that address the issue of the cost of the development and manufacture of the drug. The financial burden may be shared by all if drug research and development is paid for through taxes. Or only those who need the medication should bear the cost for that drug.

Wrap-up

- Discuss the advantages and disadvantages of the FDA process of testing drugs for approval.
- Ask students what changes, if any, they would make in the FDA process.

NAME ______ DATE ______ CLASS ______

MAKING CONNECTIONS

Chapter 9

Technology

Better Ways to Battle Bugs

Insects have always taken their share of crops meant for humans. To destroy these pests, farmers use chemicals known as pesticides. However, pesticides kill not only unwanted insects, but beneficial insects as well.

Over the years, pesticides have been seeping into the groundwater. Groundwater pollution from agriculture can contaminate our drinking water. The link between pesticides and their toxic effect on our bodies is still not totally clear. Some pesticides have been linked to cancer, immune system disorders, behavior problems, and allergies.

Pesticides increase farmers' profits by reducing insect damage to crops. Therefore, farmers whose crops suffer the effects of insects might not want to stop using pesticides. But many farmers have found alternatives.

Some farmers raise crops that insects dislike or rotate their crops to keep down pest populations in an area. Others use biological control. This involves killing pests with other insects or with bacteria. For example, farmers have found that the praying mantis eats asparagus beetles.

A recent invention for getting rid of bugs uses heat. A house or building is wrapped with large vinyl blankets and the air is heated to 60°C. All types of insects are killed by the heat. Another recent discovery is a strong-smelling mint oil that naturally repels most insects. Garlic and the oil from citrus fruits also help to repel fleas. Scientists continue to find new ways to combat pests.

Thinking About Technology Connections

1. Think of ways you can reduce the use of pesticides around your home. What could you use instead of flea collars, bug sprays, and lawn chemicals? ______

2. In what ways might farmers benefit from trying alternatives to chemical pesticides? ______

Use with Chapter 9, Section 9:1

Purpose

- The purpose of this connection is to show students some of the dangers of pesticides and how safer alternatives are possible.

Motivate

- Before introducing this connection, have students take a survey of all of the pesticides in their neighborhood grocery store. Be sure they include flea sprays and powders. Discuss the surveys in class.

Background

- Pesticides not only contribute to human morbidity. They also can affect unrelated animal life. They can interfere with an organism's reproductive ability. High levels of pesticide exposure can increase the risk of cancer and neurological disorders.
- Pesticides, when first used, increase crop yields. With continuous use, however, the pest may become resistant to the pesticide. Chemical pesticides may also eliminate a natural enemy of the pest, so the pest population actually grows.
- Environmentalists promote natural means of vermin control. For example, home owners can encourage bug-eating populations of animals such as lady bugs, praying mantises, spiders, toads, garter snakes, and birds. However, the use of biological pesticides is not necessarily hazard-free. The introduction of a new species as a pest control may result in disruption to non-targeted, beneficial species.
- Other nontoxic methods include sprinkling red chili powder and strong-smelling herbs in areas where household insects are a problem. Garlic mixed in a blender with a mild soapy liquid can be used as a spray.
- In 1993, about 6% of U.S. pesticide sales were in biological pesticides. Current trends in pesticide use focus on "integrated pest management," which incorporates both biological and chemical pesticides.

Teaching Strategies

- Explain how pesticides are dangerous to animal life and humans. Include a discussion of the decreased effectiveness of pesticide use over time.
- Discuss methods people have used to get rid of unwanted insects. These methods include using nontoxic insecticides, biological control by other insects, and rotating crops.

Answers to Student Worksheet

1. **Generating and assessing solutions:** Answers will vary, but may include herbal flea collars and garlic tablets to control fleas and mint-scented sprays to repel insects.
2. **Drawing conclusions:** Answers will vary, but may include decreased cost of pesticide, less personal exposure to toxic chemicals, and larger populations of natural predators.

Wrap-up

- Divide the students into groups and have them create posters emphasizing the dangers of pesticides and listing alternatives to harmful pesticides. Display the posters where other classes can see them.

NAME ______________________ DATE ____________ CLASS ____________

MAKING CONNECTIONS

Technology

Chapter 10

Making Paper

The United States produces more than 75 million metric tons of paper and paper products a year—that's more paper than any other country in the world. Books, magazines, paper towels, and writing paper are some of the paper items produced. Although paper products take different forms, they all begin as a plant.

In the United States, most paper begins as a large plant—a tree. Firs, pines, oaks, beeches, and other trees can be used in paper making. The process starts when the trees are cut down. They are then cut into logs and sent through a machine that removes the bark.

At this point the logs may be heated and ground into very small pieces. This is the mechanical process. Newsprint—paper for newspaper—is made this way. The logs may be cut into chips and soaked in a heated solution. This is known as the chemical process. The pages of the book you're reading probably were made using this process. No matter which process is used, the purpose is the same: to break the wood down into a mushy substance called pulp. Pulp is the material that forms paper.

Water is added to the pulp to make a water "soup." At this point, dye to make colored paper can be stirred into the mixture. The soup is fed to a large paper-making machine. One part of the machine squeezes water from the mixture. The fibers in the soup begin to form a net of paper. The net winds around big rollers that press out more water and press the fibers more closely together. Finally, the paper winds around heated rollers that remove the rest of the water.

If special finishes are needed—perhaps to keep ink from smearing—they are added after the paper dries. The last step is to roll the paper onto big reels.

Paper recycling has become very popular in the United States. In 1993, 40% of all paper was recycled. Experts predict that 60% of all paper will be recycled by the year 2000.

Thinking About Technology Connections

1. Some paper mills have their own reservoirs. Why do you think that would be important?

____

____

2. One end of a paper-making machine is called the "wet end." The other end is called the "dry end." How do you think these ends got their names? ______________________

____

____

3. Paper goes through a de-inking process before it is recycled into new paper. Why might this be important? ____

____

____

CONNECTIONS TEACHER INFORMATION

Use with Chapter 10, Sections 10:1–10:3

Purpose

- The purpose of this connection is to make students aware of all paper products people have come to depend on and to show how paper is made.

Motivate

- Hold up a dollar bill and tell students that the paper is made in only one factory in the United States and that the exact formula for making it is a carefully guarded secret.
- Speculate with students about what a class day would be like without paper.

Background

- Besides trees, other plants used to make paper include rice, hemp, jute, cotton, and bamboo. Because the United States has so many forests, trees become the obvious choice for making paper.
- Paper mills are big complexes. Besides a paper-making machine, a paper mill contains a shop where the machines are repaired, areas for storing paper and supplies, loading docks, and sometimes even an electric generator. The paper-making machines are usually housed in their own building. Some machines are quite large — longer than 110 m. These big machines are run by computers and are usually operated 7 days a week, 24 hours a day. They can produce a 900-m roll of paper every minute.
- To save both landfill room and trees (and the habitats they provide), recycling is growing in importance almost daily. Recycling one ton of newspaper is equivalent to saving eight trees. In recycling, newspaper and other kinds of paper are immersed in solution in tanks called pulpers. Once the pulp forms, it is processed into paper for items such as greeting cards, paper bags, and paper towels.
- An Executive Order issued by President Bill Clinton in 1993 requires federal agencies to buy paper products that contain a minimum of 20 percent post-consumer waste content. Paper industry experts anticipate that recycled paper products will become the norm in the near future.

Answers to Student Worksheet

1. **Drawing conclusions:** A large amount of water is needed to make the pulp soupy. A reservoir will contain a ready supply of water.
2. **Observing and inferring:** The wet end is the end in which the soupy pulp is fed. The dry end is the end where the remaining water is removed.
3. **Observing and inferring:** Inks need to be removed so that the new paper does not become tinted by the ink. Also, if the ink was left on the paper, it could change the chemical makeup of the recycled pulp.

Wrap-up

- Have students discuss ways to start a paper recycling program in the classroom. Let the students choose a plan and then, as a class, have them implement it.

NAME ______________________ DATE ____________ CLASS ____________

MAKING CONNECTIONS
Technology

Chapter 11

No-Till Farming

When you think of a farmer, you probably imagine someone who plows fields of rich, dark earth in the springtime. This kind of farmer practices *tillage* farming. But that image simply doesn't fit some farmers. These farmers practice a method of farming called *no-till* farming.

In tillage farming, the farmer uses a plow to turn the dirt over, burying the weeds and breaking up the dirt into pieces. Next, the farmer uses a machine that breaks up the large clumps of dirt the plow left. Finally, the farmer uses different machines to apply fertilizer and herbicides and plant the seeds.

In no-till farming, the farmer uses a machine that makes slits in the ground, spreads fertilizer, and plants the seeds. Sometimes the farmer does this all in one operation. What the farmer does NOT do is plow the soil.

When the crop has been harvested, the remains of the plants are left on the field. They act as a covering called *mulch*. The mulch helps to prevent the loss of soil. This is a major advantage of the no-till method. The mulch prevents the loss of as much as 90 to 95 percent of the soil that would normally be blown or washed away in a plowed field. The mulch also allows the farmer to plant on hillsides without causing excessive soil loss.

The no-till method has other advantages as well. The mulch keeps water in the soil from evaporating; that way the ground stays moist; also no-till farming requires fewer machines than the usual plowing method; it does not disturb earthworms, which feed on crop residue and fertilize the soil; and, compared with the plowing method, the farmer spends less time in planting crops.

The no-till method is well-suited to crops such as corn, which have large seeds, but it doesn't work as well with plants such as tomatoes, which have tiny seeds.

There are also some disadvantages to no-till farming. The remains of the plants that stay on the fields sometimes reseed themselves and produce weeds. In addition, large quantities of chemical fertilizers and weed killers are needed, which can be harmful to the environment.

Thinking About Technology Connections

1. Who do you think uses more fertilizer—a no-till farmer or a farmer who uses the traditional plowing method? Why? ______________________

____

____

2. What are some advantages of using less farm machinery in planting? ______________________

____

____

3. Why is using a large quantity of weed killer a disadvantage? ______________________

____

____

Use with Chapter 11, Section 11:1

Purpose

- The purpose of this technology connection is to describe an alternative farming method that decreases soil erosion.

Motivate

- Prepare a demonstration of earthworms and soil. Use an aquarium or other appropriate container. Have students observe the burrowing behavior of the worms. Ask how farmers could benefit from having such organisms in their garden soil.

Background

- U.S. farmers began using no-till farming during the 1980s. It is a primitive farming technique that is recommended today because of its effect on soil properties, as well as its benefit to energy conservation. Decreasing soil compaction, increasing organic matter in the soil, and adding to the amount of soil moisture all benefit crop production.
- No-till farming is a natural aid in the destruction of the European Corn Borer. This insect is responsible for the loss of many corn crops. In no-till systems, the corn stalks remain exposed to the air. The borers, which live in the stalks, are killed when the air turns cold in winter.
- Earthworms and nightcrawlers benefit from no-till soil. They feed on the crop residue and establish burrows that are not disturbed every year by plowing. Their presence means increased water and air infiltration. The less compacted soil also allows for increased root penetration.

Teaching Strategies

- Discuss with the students how no-till farming would affect soil characteristics, such as texture and humus content.
- Have students imagine that they are farmers who currently plow their fields. What issues would discourage a farmer from trying no-till methods?

Answers to Student Worksheet

1. **Comparing and contrasting:** No-till farmers have to use more. Spreading fertilizer over the old crops rather than directly on the ground means that some of the fertilizer never gets into the ground, and more has to be used to compensate for the unused fertilizer.
2. **Drawing conclusions:** Answers will vary. Students might suggest saving money by not buying equipment, using less energy, saving money by not having to buy fuel, or causing less pollution.
3. **Observing and inferring:** The weed killer goes into the soil and could possibly pollute nearby wells and streams. It might also poison organisms living in the soil that enrich the soil.

Wrap-up

- Divide the class into two groups. Have them debate the issue of no-till versus tillage farming.

NAME ____________________ DATE ____________ CLASS ____________

MAKING CONNECTIONS
Society

Chapter 12

Should School Buses Have Seat Belts?

Many states have laws that require drivers and passengers of motor vehicles to wear safety belts. Some new cars have air bags in addition to shoulder belts. But what about school buses?

The National Academy of Sciences (NAS) has examined the causes of school bus accidents. The NAS has also evaluated the effectiveness of safety measures, including seat belts. Their goal was to learn how to protect young people better.

The NAS and the National Academy of Engineering assembled a committee. The committee included experts in highway safety, pediatrics, school transportation, bus manufacturing, and occupant restraint systems. The study found the following.

1. Seat lap belts on school buses may reduce the number of deaths or injuries to passengers by up to 20 percent each year.
2. If all large school buses had seat belts, one life might be saved each year. Several dozen serious injuries could also be avoided. The added cost for seat belts would be more than $1,000 per bus.
3. It was found that sometimes, during an accident, seat belts would restrain children in a way that would cause their heads to jerk forward and hit the seat in front of them.
4. The study committee decided that putting seat belts in large school buses costs too much. Saving one life each year is not enough reason to spend so much money. The committee said that local school districts should not be forced to put seat belts on their buses. Some committee members did not agree. They said safety is so important that new buses should come with seat belts.
5. Some states and local school districts will choose to require seat belts in new buses. They will make sure that all school bus riders use them correctly.

What Do You Think?

1. If you had been on the study committee, what would you have said? ____________________

____

____

2. Given the results of the NAS study, do you believe schools should spend money to equip school buses with seat belts? Or should schools spend the money on other things? Explain your answer.

____

____

____

3. Should all people who travel on buses, trains, subways, and cabs have to wear safety belts? Why or why not? ____________________

____

____

CONNECTIONS TEACHER INFORMATION

Use with Chapter 12, Section 12:1

Purpose

- This purpose of this connection is to help students develop an understanding of safety features on motor vehicles. It will also introduce them to the concept of cost versus benefit in safety issues.

Motivate

- Poll the students in the class to see how many normally wear a seat belt when riding in a car. What factors affect their decisions to use a seat belt? Would they be more or less likely to use a seat belt when riding a school bus?

Background

- The purpose of seat belts is to prevent passengers from being thrown out of a vehicle in a crash. They also keep passengers from hitting the windshield or dashboards. Many safety officials argue that buses are already the safest way to travel. Bus designs provide better protection than seat belts during a collision. Buses are equipped with high back safety seats, steel barriers that surround the gas tanks so they don't leak or explode on impact, and a roof that won't collapse in a roll over accident. Buses are estimated to be eight times safer than cars.
- The automotive industry has advanced beyond using lap belts. Lap belts have proved to be inadequate in preventing injuries. They have been replaced by the shoulder harness with cross strap and air bags. Yet it is the lap belt that is being advocated for installation in buses. The pupil transportation industry recommends further research in passive restraint designs.

Teaching Strategies

- Have students compare the following restraint systems: lap belts, shoulder harnesses with cross straps, air bags, and fully padded, high-backed safety seats. They should include in their consideration the relative effectiveness of each system in preventing injuries. Compare the appropriateness of each system for private vehicles versus public transportation. Students may present their information as a report or as a poster.
- Show a safety film that illustrates the effectiveness of seat belts and air bags. Have students debate the effectiveness of restraint systems versus their enormous cost.

Answers to Student Worksheet

1. **Generating and assessing solutions:** Possible answers could be that students want a safe environment or that safety belts can be uncomfortable and restrict movement that may lead to further injury.
2. **Drawing conclusions:** Schools *should* equip school buses with seat belts. Student safety is the most important priority. Schools *should not* equip buses with seat belts. Not even a selt belt can assure a perfectly safe environment. The money would be better spent on items such as books or computers.
3. **Developing a perspective:** Yes—Safety belts save lives, and insurance costs could go down. No—Seat belts are uncomfortable. Sometimes they can cause injury. People should have the right to choose if they wear them or not.

Wrap-up

- Have students conduct a survey of the other students on whether they think that seat belts should be installed on school buses. If their school bus did have seat belts, would the students want to wear them? Why or why not?

MAKING CONNECTIONS
Society

Chapter 13

Space Law

Before the first satellite was launched into space, people didn't pay much attention to who might own the moon, Venus, or a yet undiscovered planet. When the Soviet satellite *Sputnik I* was launched in 1957, the world was propelled into the space age. It suddenly became important to write laws to regulate the ownership of property in space and to hold countries responsible for their actions there.

Laws on space are international laws—they apply to all nations. This is why, in 1957, President Eisenhower suggested to members of the United Nations that they begin to write rules governing activities in outer space.

The first point the nations agreed on dealt with territories in space. Nations are not allowed to lay claim to territories in space as they have done in the past on Earth. Just because a planet is uninhabited doesn't give a country the right to claim ownership.

In 1957, an Outer Space Committee was formed. The Committee drafted an agreement, signed in 1967, to ban nuclear weapons tests in space.

In 1967, 63 nations signed the Treaty on Principles Governing the Activities of States in the Exploration and Use of Outer Space, Including the Moon and Other Celestial Bodies —also called the Outer Space Treaty. The treaty consists of twelve articles. Some of the articles repeat rules agreed to before. Others cover new areas. One article prohibits military activities in outer space. Another requires countries to be responsible for the vehicles and equipment they send into space and for any damage they may cause. Still another calls on all countries to aid astronauts in trouble.

Some treaties, including agreements about who can use the resources found on planets in outer space, have not yet been worked out.

What Do You Think?

1. When international laws have to be written, why is it helpful to have an organization like the United Nations? ____________________

____

____

2. Would the U.N. treaties apply to countries that don't belong to the U.N. or beings from other planets? Explain. ____________________

____

____

CONNECTIONS TEACHER INFORMATION

Use with Chapter 13, Section 13:1

Purpose

- The purpose of this connection is to make students aware that laws are needed to regulate activities in outer space, just as they are needed to regulate life on Earth.

Motivate

- Discuss with students how laws help regulate their lives and resolve disputes.
- Ask students what kind of laws might be needed to control countries' actions when their astronauts explore outer space.

Background

- Launched into space on October 4, 1957, *Sputnik I* was an unmanned satellite that orbited Earth until 1958. Its launching marked the beginning of the space race between the United States and the U.S.S.R. After the U.S.S.R. launched *Sputnik I* and the United States launched *Explorer I* in 1958, both countries became extremely interested in international space agreements.
- Some of the articles from the Outer Space Treaty that are not covered in the connection deal with keeping peace in space, protecting the environment of planetary bodies in outer space and of Earth, and inspecting other countries' space vehicles and equipment on the moon and on other planetary bodies.
- A further U.N. agreement, the Agreement on the Rescue and Return of Astronauts and the Return of Objects Launched into Space, was signed into 1968. It reiterated and expanded points already agreed to in the Outer Space Treaty.

Teaching Strategies

- Explain that there are international laws that govern people's activities on the seas. For example, one country cannot exercise power over a foreign ship if the ship is on the high seas. It can, though, if that ship is within twelve miles of the country's shoreline. Discuss the idea that laws are needed in outer space to regulate the activities of countries there.

Answers to Student Worksheet

1. **Developing a perspective:** The United Nations provides a central place where many nations can meet together.
2. **Drawing conclusions:** No. Since the countries that don't belong to the U.N. and the beings from other planets haven't agreed to the treaties, the treaties wouldn't apply to them.

Wrap-up

- Have the class write two laws, perhaps about keeping extraterrestrial bodies environmentally safe.

NAME ____________ DATE ____________ CLASS ____________

MAKING CONNECTIONS
Society

Chapter 14

Protecting an Aquifer

Where do you get your water? If you live in the country, you probably have a well and get your water from an aquifer.

Imagine that you live in a small country town. A few new businesses have come into the town. Business owners are beginning to talk about building a new highway. Farmers from the region discuss the need for a place to feed cattle, called a feedlot, near the town. A real estate developer starts buying land at the east end of the town. The developer hopes the new businesses will bring in additional workers who will be looking for homes. The real estate agent talks to a builder. They discuss starting construction of a new development that will include new homes. They talk about sinking wells and adding sewers for the new development.

Another group in the town begins to worry. The community draws its water from a system of wells, all of which are tapped into one good aquifer. "What will happen," these citizens ask, "when more wells are sunk? How will new homes and businesses affect the amount of water in the aquifer? Won't adding new sewers mean that the sewage treatment plant will have to be enlarged? Will the feedlot, the new highway, and the bigger sewage treatment plant harm the quality of the water in the aquifer?"

These concerned citizens might consider asking the Environmental Protection Agency for help. The EPA is an agency of the federal government that helps protect the environment. The agency can help protect the aquifer if it provides more than half of the drinking water for the community and if there is danger of contamination to the water in the aquifer. The EPA can then classify the aquifer as a "sole" (single) or "principal" (main) source aquifer. Once the aquifer is classified this way, government agencies are forbidden to give any help to a project that could harm the aquifer. Ordinarily, construction of highways, sewage plants, and sometimes even businesses and homes is done with the help of government loans.

The small community may be beginning a "water war." To fight this war, people in the town will have to agree on a plan that will preserve their aquifer.

What Do You Think?

1. How could a highway affect an aquifer? What is on a highway that could be carried by the water that runs off the highway and soaks into the ground? ____________

____

2. How could a feedlot for cattle or a sewage plant affect groundwater? ____________

____

3. How would an increase in the population affect the aquifer? ____________

____

4. Do you think the town described in the above discussion can afford to grow? Give arguments on both sides of the question. Then explain what you think would be the best solution.

____

CONNECTIONS TEACHER INFORMATION

Use with Chapter 14, Section 14:3

Purpose

- To help students understand the effect of the development of communities on aquifers and how they can be protected from overuse and pollutants.

Motivate

- Have students make a list of possible types and sources of contaminants to drinking water in their county.

Background

- It is important to protect aquifers that are close to the surface, especially those with top layers of porous sand, since these are most easily contaminated. Studies show that hazardous materials have been dumped into many abandoned sand and gravel quarries.
- In Dayton, Ohio, in 1987, a paint factory caught fire. The plant was built on an aquifer that supplied water for more than 680 000 people in the Dayton metropolitan area. After the fire, the groundwater was contaminated. The paint company paid more then $10 million in groundwater clean-up costs. In Dade County, Florida, the community enacted one of the first underground water protection policies. In 1981, protected areas were named. No new business that used or made a hazardous material could be built in the area.

Teaching Strategies

- Explain to students that an aquifer stores water underground in permeable rock. The water level changes with the amount of rain, temperature, and amount of water taken out by wells. As population increases, so does the potential for pollution from transportation, industry, animal waste, pesticides, and fertilizers.

Answers to Student Worksheet

1. **Observing and inferring:** Highway construction can affect an aquifer chiefly through its contamination of the water. Water runs off a highway and soaks into the ground. This water carries traces of oil and gasoline left on a heavily used highway plus any contaminants spilled on the highway.
2. **Recognizing cause and effect:** Waste from a feedlot could contaminate ground water and so could chemicals added to cattle feed that would soak into the ground. If not properly treated, sewage can contaminate groundwater.
3. **Making inferences:** An increase in the population would result in faster use of water in the aquifer, which could cause the water supply to decrease.
4. **Generating and assessing solutions:** Answers might include: Arguments for growth include the need for businesses to keep a community alive, the ability of the aquifer to provide enough water, and control of contaminants. Arguments against growth would be that the aquifer must be protected or the people currently living there would find themselves with an unsafe or dwindling water supply.

Wrap-up

- Students should imagine themselves as part of Congress. As elected officials, they have a duty to the people in their district. Have them draft a proposal for a law to protect the aquifer in their district. Remember to include agriculture, industry, and residential interests as well as a method to pay for the protection.

NAME ______________________ DATE ____________ CLASS ____________

MAKING CONNECTIONS

Society

Chapter 15

Shoreline Erosion

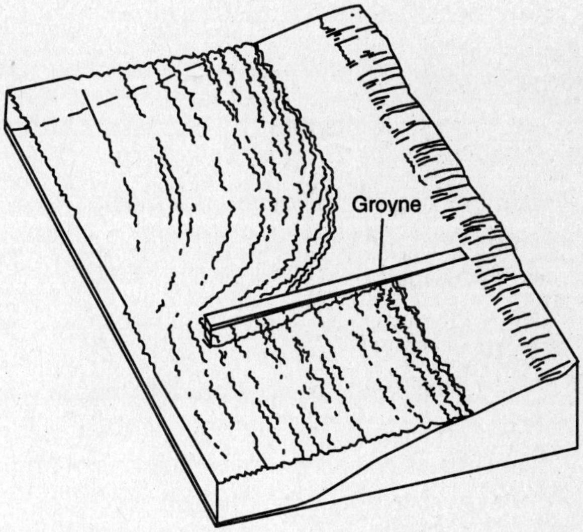

When wind blows over the ocean, water is forced to move. This movement is called waves. Under the water, there is also movement. Underwater movement is called a current. Both waves and currents affect objects on the shore.

Shoreline erosion occurs through the combined effects of waves and currents. Waves will erode a shoreline, especially during storms. Shoreline erosion causes millions of dollars of damage to property and houses each year. This type of erosion causes the loss of land and can destroy buildings near the shoreline. Land loss of up to three meters per year has occurred in some areas on the southern shore of Lake Erie.

People try to control beach erosion by building structures to slow it down. Structures called groynes are used to protect the shoreline by trapping sand as it is carried away by waves and currents traveling parallel to the shore. Groynes are straight structures made of asphalt and sand that stick out into the water. A groyne will trap sand on the side from which the current is moving. The accumulated sand protects that part of the shoreline from erosion. On the opposite side, currents will remove sand from the beach. Groynes are not a permanent solution to erosion problems. However, they provide more time for other steps to be taken to protect shoreline property.

What Do You Think?

1. Use the library to find out what factors determine the rate of erosion of a shoreline.

____

____

2. Much wave erosion takes place during storms. Why do you think this occurs?

____

____

3. What are some of the advantages and disadvantages of living along a seashore or a lakeshore?

____

____

____

CONNECTIONS TEACHER INFORMATION

Use with Chapter 15, Section 15:1

Purpose

- The purpose of this connection is to help the students understand beach erosion and how humans attempt to control it.

Motivate

- Have the students identify coastal areas that are undergoing rapid beach erosion. Are many of these areas developed? What happens to the shoreline in the areas that are developed?

Background

- Beaches exist due to erosion. During the last ice age, material dug out of rocks by glaciers was eroded away by streams, worn down in size, and deposited on the beaches. These beaches grew over thousands of years. Now, erosion of the beaches is taking place at a greater pace than deposition.
- Beaches are always changing by a process called littoral drift. Sand and other materials removed from one place are left on a beach somewhere else. Severe localized beach erosion is caused by storms and rising sea levels.
- Humans also cause erosion. We disturb vegetation that stabilizes dunes and those dunes are more apt to erode. Dams and reservoirs inland cut off the sand before it reaches the beaches and prevent deposition.
- As beaches erode, more wetlands are destroyed. Toxic waste sites could be flooded and groundwater contaminated. Salt water could also contaminate aquifers as salt water moves inland.
- Jetties, groynes, and seawalls are the most common way to control beach erosion. Jetties are used to control erosion of the inlets. Sea walls are built in front of the beaches to prevent waves from reaching the beach and eroding it. Groynes are built perpendicular to the beach to trap sand on the beach. These structures are not always effective. The only way to build up a beach is to truck in the sand. This can be very costly.

Teaching Strategies

- Compare pictures of beaches that have been developed to pictures of beaches that have been left in their natural state. What are the differences? Are there any similarities? If there are pictures of a beach before it was developed, compare the before and after.
- Talk about reasons that people want to develop beach areas. Who benefits and who loses from this development? Are there any cases where both sides have won?

Answers to Student Worksheet

1. **Distinguishing relevant from irrelevant facts:** The rate of erosion is affected by the kind of materials the land and rocks are made of, wind direction, water current direction, and the use of protective structures.
2. **Making inferences, predictions, or interpretations:** The waves are stronger, more powerful, and more frequent during storms so they can erode more material than during calm weather.
3. **Comparing and contrasting:** Advantages include popular scenery and recreation. Disadvantages include storm damage and shoreline erosion from waves.

Wrap-up

- Have the students discuss shoreline erosion. What will happen if sea level continues to rise and erosion increases? What coastal cities are in danger of being flooded? What can we do to prevent it?

NAME ______________________ DATE ______________ CLASS ______________

MAKING CONNECTIONS
Society

Chapter 16

The Harlequin Duck—An Environmental Indicator

Sometimes damage that has occurred to the environment is easy to spot. But when it isn't, scientists may look to an indicator species to gauge the health of a particular habitat. An indicator species is an organism that is very sensitive to changes in the environment. The harlequin duck of the North Atlantic and Northern Pacific Oceans is just such a species.

Harlequin ducks spend most of the year in the rough, cold, intertidal waters of the ocean coast. But the ducks have an unusual migration pattern. Each spring, they swim miles upstream to the fast-flowing, freshwater stream where they were born. There the ducks mate and lay their eggs. In the fall the ducks fly back to their ocean home.

Once, there were a great many harlequin ducks in this rugged environment. Today, the harlequin population is decreasing.

Overhunting of harlequins has caused population decline. So has change in the habitat of the ducks.

Harlequins seem to be especially bothered by noise and human contact. Harlequin birth rates fall dramatically in areas where hikers and boaters are common. Changes in stream and river flow, caused by the construction of dams, industries, and marinas also disrupt harlequin breeding patterns. These changes upset nesting, since harlequins try to return to the same inland stream each year.

Large populations of harlequin ducks once lived in the cool shoreline waters of Prince William Sound, on the coast of Alaska. In 1989, the *Exxon Valdez* oil tanker ran aground in the Sound, spilling 11 million gallons of oil and killing otters, seals, barnacles, fish, mussels, and harlequin ducks.

Today, evidence of the *Exxon Valdez* disaster is less apparent. Many other species thrive in Prince William Sound. But the population of harlequin ducks has not returned to its earlier level. Worldwide, the population of harlequin ducks is now so small that the harlequin duck may be placed on the endangered species list.

Thinking About Society Connections

1. What is an indicator species? ______________________________

____

2. What factors threaten the survival of the harlequin duck? ______________________________

____

3. What evidence suggests that the environment in Prince William Sound has not recovered fully from the 1989 oil spill? ______________________________

____

Use with Chapter 16, Section 16:3

Purpose

- The purpose of this connection is to demonstrate that organisms may be indicators of environmental problems.

Motivate

- Have students pick a favorite aquatic animal and write its name on a sheet of paper. Ask students to describe the environment in which the animal lives, including any specific adaptations relevant to the animal's habitat. Students should save their animal descriptions to use again in the wrap-up section.

Background

- Extinction is a natural process. However, the number of organisms threatened with extinction today has been greatly influenced by human action and damage to the environment. For example, loss of habitat due to construction and farming, and pollution resulting from the burning of fossil fuels, ocean dumping, and use of pesticides all have been linked to a loss in biodiversity.
- Oil spills are a serious threat to aquatic animals. Shellfish and other plants and animals that live in the water are sometimes killed, as are shoreline animals and waterfowl that rely on ocean organisms for food. Aquatic mammals and waterfowl are affected by oil spills in two other ways. First, chemicals contained in the ingested oil serve as toxins, disrupting normal cell function. In addition, as oil coats the fur and feathers of animals, the animals become weighted down by the oil and can drown.

Teaching Strategies

- Obtain pictures from magazines and newspapers related to the *Exxon Valdez* oil spill in Prince William Sound. Use the pictures to discuss the environmental damage suffered by the area as a result of the spill. Point out the numbers and types of organisms that were directly affected by the spill.

Answers to Student Worksheet

1. An indicator species is a type of organism that is sensitive to environmental change and may be used to identify an area that is unhealthy.
2. Factors threatening the harlequin duck include overhunting, human contact, disruption to river and stream course, and pollution.
3. The harlequin duck population in the Prince William Sound area has not returned to its earlier size.

Wrap-up

- Ask students to refer to the aquatic animal they selected earlier in the lesson. Have students explain how an oil spill such as that of the *Exxon Valdez* might affect their animal.

NAME ____________ DATE ________ CLASS ________

MAKING CONNECTIONS
Technology

Chapter 17

Weather Forecasting with Radar

Scientists can use radio waves to predict when a storm is likely to arrive in an area. A radar set sends out radio signals that bounce off raindrops or other moisture in the air and return to the set. By measuring how long it takes for the signals to return, an observer can tell where the storm is and how much moisture is in the air.

The radar used in weather forecasting can show the size and density of raindrops in the air. Knowing this helps forecasters warn people of heavy rainfall and hailstorms.

A forecaster is able to predict the path of a storm by locating the storm, then every few minutes checking its location again to see where it has moved. The forecaster can also tell how fast the storm is moving.

Once the speed and direction of travel are known, it is possible to predict where a storm will go next and when it will arrive. If people in an area know when a storm is coming, they can prepare for it, preventing injury to themselves or damage to their property.

The radar used in weather forecasting is the same type (Doppler radar) as that used by police to catch speeding motorists. Most states have several sites where weather is monitored by radar. The radar units scan the sky for 150 miles in all directions and make records of cloud patterns. Each station's records are sent to the National Meteorological Center in Washington, D.C., where they are put together with other stations' records to make a national weather map. Maps are updated every hour.

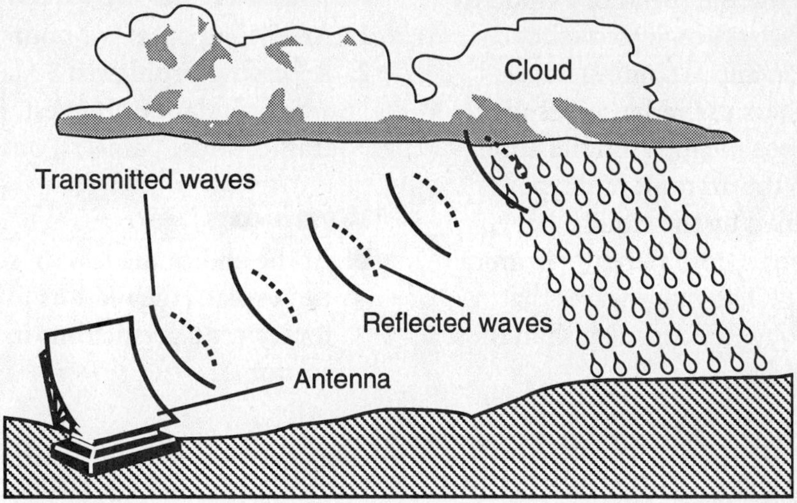

Thinking About Technology Connections

1. If you learned that a tornado were coming toward your home at 40 miles per hour, and it was 20 miles from your home, how much time would you have to find a safe place?

____

2. List as many reasons as can you think of for needing to be able to predict weather.

____

____

CONNECTIONS TEACHER INFORMATION

Use with Chapter 17, Sections 17:1–17:2

Purpose

- The purpose of this connection is to show how radar waves are used to help predict weather.

Motivate

- Show students a videotape of a weather forecast with Doppler radar maps. Ask students how they think the system works.

Background

- Weather forecasters began using radar to determine the location of clouds in the 1940s. A radar transmitter sends out signals that travel through the atmosphere until they encounter some sort of resistance, such as water droplets or ice. They are then reflected back at a higher frequency if the cloud is approaching the transmitter, or at a lower frequency if it is moving away. It is possible to estimate the speed of a cloud by measuring the difference in frequency between outgoing and incoming waves.
- Weather forecasters use radar waves to detect the presence of clouds in the atmosphere and even the amount and types of moisture contained by the clouds. For example, hail shows up differently from rain on a radar screen. The radar waves that reflect off hailstones are stronger than those reflected off raindrops.
- Other information can be derived from radar readings. By mapping the path of a tornado for a short distance, it is possible to compare the early progress of a current tornado to paths historically followed by other tornadoes.

Teaching Strategies

- Show how a tennis ball bounces back from a wall, relating this to the action of radar waves. Use a photo flash and a mirror to demonstrate how light waves bounce back from surfaces. Go to an empty auditorium or gymnasium and have the students shout or clap and listen for the reflected sounds. Explain the similarities between these demonstrations and the way in which radar is bounced off clouds.

Answers to Student Worksheet

1. **Analyzing data:** 1/2 hours.
2. **Assessing problems:** So farmers can know when to plant or harvest, for scheduling air traffic, house painters, outdoor sports events

Wrap-up

- At the end of the lesson, see if the students can explain the reasons for the weather forecaster's predictions in the Motivate section.

NAME ______________________ DATE ______________ CLASS ______________

MAKING CONNECTIONS
Technology

Chapter 18

Measuring Earth Movements with Lasers

Earthquakes are sudden, large movements along cracks in Earth's surface. Small movements along these cracks can help scientists predict where and when an earthquake might occur. But it is very hard to measure these small movements. Sometimes, the movements are less than one-half inch per year. Common mapping techniques are not very accurate for such small movements.

In the 1960s, surveyors started using lasers to study and measure Earth's surface. These special tools are called *laser ranging devices.* The laser sends a narrow beam of light to a reflector target on the other side of a crack in Earth's surface. The light bounces off the reflector target and returns. The speed of light and the original distance between the laser and the reflector target are known. So if there is any movement along the crack, the distance the light travels also changes. With this device, surveyors can measure movements as little as one-fifteenth of an inch.

Now, lasers are being used with an orbiting satellite named *Lageos,* which is short for *Laser Geodynamic Satellite.* A laser station is placed on one side of a crack in Earth's surface. This station sends a light beam up to *Lageos.* The beam reflects back to a receiving station on the other side of the crack. A computer then calculates whether or not there has been movement.

Scientists study the information they get from the laser ranging devices as well as information they have about where earthquakes have happened in the past. With this information, scientists can see patterns in how small Earth movements relate to earthquakes. These patterns may help them predict future earthquakes.

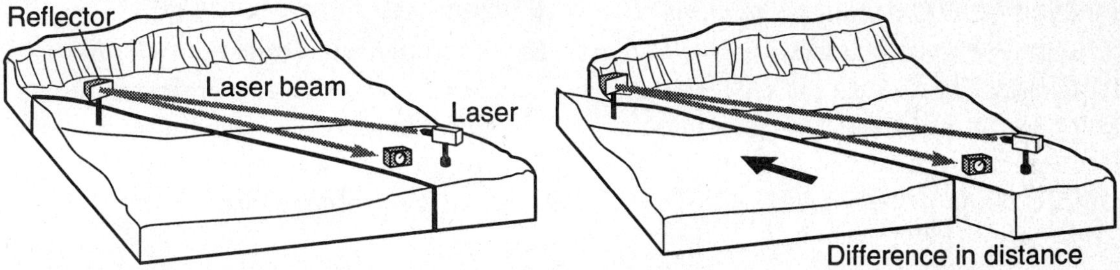

Thinking About Technology Connections

1. Why do we use lasers to measure Earth movements? ______________________

____

2. How could scientists use the patterns of Earth's movement to predict earthquakes?

____

____

3. What other uses can you think of for lasers? ______________________

____

____

CONNECTIONS TEACHER INFORMATION

Use with Chapter 18, Section 18:3

Purpose

- The purpose of this connection is to show students how modern technology can be used to study and help predict earthquakes.

Motivate

- Discuss how lasers are used in science fiction. In "Star Trek," for example, a phaser (a form of laser) is used as a weapon. But they are also used in surgery and communications.

Background

- Light from the sun or electric bulbs usually travels in all directions. However, the light from a laser is directional; it travels in only one direction. This allows great control of the light and makes lasers useful in communications, industry, medicine, military operations, and scientific research.
- The word *laser* is short for *Light Amplification by Stimulated Emission of Radiation.* There are many types of lasers, and the color and intensity of the light depends on the laser's use and construction. Most lasers are not used for destruction, as is often the case on television or the movies.

Teaching Strategies

- Explain to students the importance of predicting earthquakes. Use weather prediction as an analogy, especially the prediction of hurricanes and tornados.
- Briefly describe how a laser works. In general terms, you can explain that a laser produces a focused light beam while ordinary light sources do not.

Answers to Student Worksheet

1. **Drawing conclusions:** Because light from a laser moves so fast, even slight movement of Earth's surface can be detected.
2. **Drawing conclusions:** If there are many vibrations at a particular point on Earth's surface, this could mean an earthquake is starting or about to occur.
3. **Making inferences, predictions, or interpretations:** Answers may vary, but could include microsurgery, weapons, or compact disc players.

Wrap-up

- Ask students to come up with an original use for lasers. Start by brainstorming a list of problems. Then have the students form groups, select a problem from the list, and solve the problem with a laser.

NAME ______________________ DATE ______________ CLASS ______________

MAKING CONNECTIONS

Society

Chapter 19

Mariculture in the Bay of Fundy

The Bay of Fundy is located between New Brunswick and Nova Scotia and has the highest tides in the world. The tides in the Bay of Fundy make it ideal for raising Atlantic salmon. Saltwater farming of this kind is called mariculture.

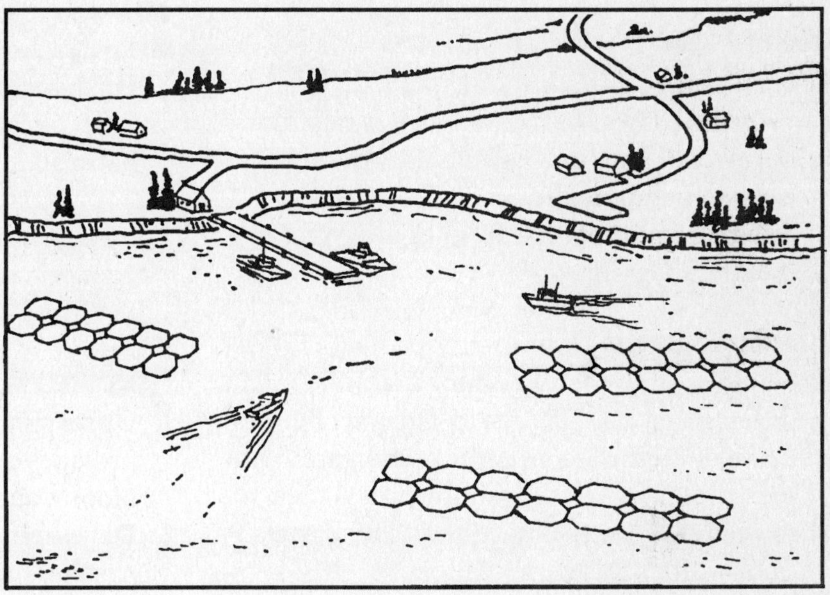

In order to raise Atlantic salmon, you need a clean, rich oxygen supply, which the tides bring in twice a day. The tides also take out uneaten food and dirt. Organisms called algal blooms can give off poisons and become a problem in mariculture. But the tides prevent this by washing away poisons with the tide.

Salmon are a cold-water fish, so temperature is also an important part of raising salmon. When water doesn't move, it separates into layers of different temperatures. Because the tides move in and out, these layers mix and create a uniform temperature. The water stays slightly above freezing during the winter and slightly below 15°C in the summer.

Farming of Atlantic salmon began in the 1960s in Norway. Ocean farmers used the narrow inlets of the sea there for salmon pens. The pens frequently resemble chains of eight-sided links. In the late 1970s, farming of salmon moved across the Atlantic to the Bay of Fundy. It has been much more successful there because of the strength of the tides.

What Do You Think?

1. Give several reasons why the Bay of Fundy is such a good place to raise salmon.

____

____

____

2. Can you think of any other aquatic animals that are raised on a farm? Give some examples.

____

____

____

CONNECTIONS TEACHER INFORMATION

Use with Chapter 19, Section 19:3

Purpose

- The purpose of this connection is to show how ocean farmers take advantage of tides to raise salmon.

Motivate

- Have students think about where the food in stores comes from and how it is raised or developed. Encourage students, working as a class, to outline the process of getting different kinds of food from their origins to the dinner table.

Background

- Salmon farming on a commercial scale began about 20 years ago in Norway. Because of their taste, Atlantic salmon are prized. In farming the salmon, clean, cold, oxygen-rich water is necessary. The Bay of Fundy offers this combination.
- Briefly, the salmon farming process is as follows. The brood "hens" are stripped of their eggs. Then, a sperm-bearing fluid is placed in buckets with the eggs and fresh water. After fertilization, the eggs are incubated for six to eight weeks. Then the salmon are placed in pens and kept for about 3 1/2 years.

Teaching Strategies

- Review how the moon causes tides on Earth through the pull of gravity. Discuss how tides can be either beneficial or harmful.
- For a class activity, ask students to write a brief description of a shoreline as the tide goes out. Their description should focus on the living things in or around the water.

Answers to Student Worksheet

1. **Observing and inferring:** The Bay of Fundy provides oxygen, cleans itself, prevents algal bloom, and offers a uniform temperature.
2. **Developing a perspective:** catfish, crayfish, oysters, shrimp, trout

Wrap-up

- Have students brainstorm about how Earth would be different without the moon. Students may write a story, create a poster, or give a presentation on their ideas.